The local newspape
competition for schoo.
The child who found the oldest and
most exciting treasure would win a
trip for two to Space Fun Park.

'You can find buried treasure
anywhere,' the newspaper had said.

CALLING ALL
TREASURE
HUNTERS

You can find buried treasure anywhere ...
We are running a competition for the child who can find the oldest and most exciting treasure in the area. The lucky winner will get a trip for two to Space Fun Park!

'Let's have a look at that coin,'
said Omar.

Omar spun it in his fingers. 'Wow!'
he said, 'it *does* look old!'

Omar passed it back to Kerry who
was jumping about with excitement.

'It's a real treasure coin,' she grinned.
'Come on!' she shouted. 'We're going to
show this to Mr Hart right now.'

Cornflake Coin

Jonny Zucker

Illustrated by Martin Remphry

OXFORD
UNIVERSITY PRESS

1
The find

'Look!' cried Kerry. She was scrabbling in the long grass.

'What is it?' asked Omar.

It was lunchtime, and Kerry and Omar were out in the school field.

Kerry held up something round and shiny. It gleamed in the sun.

'It's a coin!' she said. 'It looks really old.'

'Let's take it to Mr Hart,' said Omar. 'Then he'll put it in for the competition. You never know, you might win.'

2

The real thing?

Mr Hart was sitting at his desk when
Kerry and Omar burst into the classroom.

'What's going on?' asked Mr Hart,
looking up.

'I just found this on the field!' panted
Kerry. 'Will you enter it for the buried
treasure competition?'

She dropped the shiny coin on to
Mr Hart's desk.

Mr Hart rubbed the coin. Then he looked at the writing on it. Kerry and Omar stared at him.

'If you look at the edge of the coin,' he said, 'you can see the words *Fun Start*.'

Kerry and Omar looked at each other.

'You mean like *Fun Start*, the cereal?' asked Kerry.

Mr Hart nodded. 'Yes, Kerry. This coin looks real, but it's a copy. It's a free gift from a cereal packet. I'm really sorry.'

Kerry felt her heart sink. Mr Hart saw her face.

'Cheer up, Kerry,' he said. 'There's plenty of time to find some real treasure before the competition closes.'

Kerry and Omar walked back across the classroom. They were about to go out when they heard someone behind them.

It was Matt Thorn. He was always saying mean things.

Now he was laughing at Kerry.

3

Cereal laughter

The next day all the class knew about
Kerry's cereal packet coin. Matt Thorn
had told everyone.

'Kerry wanted to enter a *cornflake* coin
in the treasure competition!' Matt
smirked. Everyone laughed, but Matt
laughed the loudest.

'That's enough, Matt,' said Mr Hart.

'Don't let Matt bother you,'
whispered Omar, but Kerry had gone
red in the face. She was angry with
Matt and cross with herself. How could
she have been so stupid to think that
the coin was *real* treasure?

Over the next few days everyone talked non-stop about the treasure competition. Lots of children brought in things they'd found at home or in their gardens.

Kara brought in some yellowy old photos, Ben dug up an old glass bottle and Jas brought in an old children's book with a green cover.

Then Matt Thorn showed everyone a white and blue china teacup. He'd taken it out of his gran's cupboard.

Mr Hart looked at the teacup very carefully. 'This is *very* old, Matt,' he said. 'I think it's got a good chance of winning the competition.'

Matt chuckled proudly.

Kerry glared at him. There was no way she was going to let *him* win.

At the end of the day she hurried out of school.

'What are you doing?' asked Omar, trying to keep up with her.

'We have to find something older than Matt's teacup,' Kerry said.

Back home, Kerry asked her mum to take them to the park.

Kerry and Omar looked under benches, in bushes and next to the fence.

They found half a pencil and an old football.

Then Kerry asked her mum if they could go down by the canal.

'What are you two up to?' asked Kerry's mum.

'Nothing,' said Kerry.

By the canal, they looked under the bridge and along the path. They found a broken doll and six empty sweet packets.

Half an hour later, they were both tired and fed up.

'Let's go home,' said Omar.

Kerry nodded glumly. 'Let's forget about the stupid competition,' she said.

4

Barker digs for gold

At the weekend, Kerry and Omar were in the park having a picnic with Kerry's mum and dad. Kerry was still in a bad mood.

'What's up with you?' asked her mum.

Kerry shrugged her shoulders.

'I'm taking Barker for a walk before he digs any more holes,' her dad said. 'Why don't you two come with me?'

'Don't feel like it,' said Kerry.

'Come on!' said Dad. 'We can go up the big hill where they're building that new café.'

Kerry groaned. She stood up and took Barker's lead.

Ten minutes later, they were at the
top of the hill. There was a huge,
muddy hole in the ground where the
café was going to be built.

Dad went to look at the yellow
digger parked under some trees.

Barker suddenly started howling and
pulling away from Kerry.

She dropped his lead. In a second he had raced down into the hole and started digging.

'Maybe he's found some real treasure!' Kerry shouted.

'I bet it's just an old bone,' said Omar. 'He's always digging up something.'

Barker scrabbled about and dug up some bits of wood. Then he trotted over to Kerry. There was something in his mouth.

The look of excitement vanished from Kerry's face. 'Just our luck,' she grumbled, 'it's another of those stupid cornflake coins.'

'Let's keep it, anyway,' said Omar.

'*You* can if you want to,' shrugged Kerry, handing him the coin, 'but I've had enough of cornflake coins.'

Just then, Kerry's dad called them over. It was time to go. Omar slipped the coin into his pocket. Kerry grabbed Barker's lead and they all went back down the hill.

5

And the winner is...

On Friday, Mr Hart packed up all of the treasure that the class had found. He put it into a big cardboard box. 'The competition closes today,' he said. 'I'll drop this off at the newspaper after school. Does anyone have anything else?'

Everyone shook their heads.

Then Omar felt a coin in his back pocket. It was the one Barker had found.

'Kerry's dog found this,' he said, passing the coin to Mr Hart.

'It's another cornflake coin!' called Matt Thorn. Everyone laughed.

'Why did you have to bring that out?' hissed Kerry crossly.

A few days later, the whole school
was packed into the hall. A tall woman
stood up.

'My name is Clare Fenton,' she said.
'I'm the editor of the local newspaper.
I'm very glad to tell you that someone
from this school has won our buried
treasure competition.'

There was a ripple of excitement in the hall. Everyone looked at Matt Thorn. They'd all heard about his teacup. Matt was grinning from ear to ear. He was getting ready to collect his prize.

'The winner is …' said the editor, 'Kerry Robinson! Kerry has found a real Roman coin.'

There were gasps of surprise and then everyone began clapping. Kerry stood up in shock. She grabbed Omar's elbow. 'You're coming with me,' she said.

The only person not clapping was Matt Thorn.

'Well done!' beamed the editor. 'You will be on the front page of our newspaper this week!'

The editor handed Kerry the tickets for Space Fun Park and smiled, 'Mr Hart said your dog Barker found the coin.'

'Barker found it,' replied Kerry, 'but Omar helped too. He stopped me throwing it away. I thought it was a cornflake coin.'

'Well, it's a good thing that Barker knew what it was,' laughed the editor. 'I think he and Omar should be on the front page, too, don't you?'

On the way back to class, everyone wanted to talk to Kerry and Omar. Matt Thorn walked behind, his face looking like a thundercloud.

Mr Hart smiled at Kerry. 'Barker dug up the real thing, didn't he?'

'Yes,' Kerry nodded. 'It's a good thing he knows the difference between a *treasure* coin and a *cornflake* coin.'

She looked at Omar and they both grinned.

About the author

As a child I once found a shiny gold coin inside a cereal packet. I was incredibly excited because I thought it was a real Roman coin. When I discovered it was a copy I was so disappointed. I soon got over it though and in the end I collected every coin in the series.

I live in north London and as well as writing children's books, I strum my guitar, play with my two young sons and dream of playing for Arsenal one day.